Garfield's
Guide
To
BEHAVING BADLY

JIM DAVIS

RAVETTE PUBLISHING

D0184892

ODIE AND I ARE PLAYING "PROSPECTING FOR GOLD"

PUSH!

NOW WE'RE PLAYING "PACK MULE GETS TOO CLOSE TO THE LEDGE"

JIM DAVIS 4-28

I THINK JON'S MAD AT ME

BUT, HE SHOULD KNOW BETTER THAN TO WAKE ME SO EARLY IN THE MORNING

MARE MAR MY LIPS?!

I THINK YOUR LIPS ARE UNDER THE SOFA

JIM DAVIS 4-13

NICE SPACE HELMET, GARFIELD

THANK YOU

WHERE'S MY GOLDFISH?

EXPLORING (BURP) NEW FRONTIERS.

Jim Davis 3-3

TWO ASTRONAUTS HOVERING ABOVE A HOSTILE PLANET

ONE OPTS TO STAY ABOARD WHILE THE OTHER BEAMS DOWN TO THE SURFACE

Jim Davis 3-4

© 1993 United Feature Syndicate, Inc.

WELL, I THINK I'LL EAT A BIRD!

I GOTTA STOP TALKING TO MYSELF

EVER WAKE UP FEELING DEPRESSED, GARFIELD?

MAYBE IT'S MY UNEVENTFUL LIFE

OR MAYBE IT'S BECAUSE YOU GLUED MY HAND TO MY FACE!!

SURE, BLAME ME

THAT'S THE BIGGEST SLINGSHOT I'VE EVER SEEN

I HATE BIRDS

I HAVE A HAIR DRYER, AND I'M DANGEROUS!

JIM DAVIS 12-12

JIM DAVIS 8-4

PRETTY GOOD HANG TIME ON THAT KICK

WHAP!

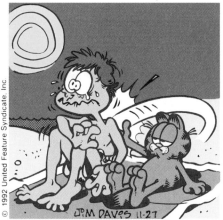

WHA...?!

ALL MY SOCKS HAVE HOLES IN THEM!

SOUNDS LIKE A JOB FOR THE MASKED AVENGERS!

FETCH THE INVISIBLE BALL, ODIE!

I LOVE THAT DOG

© 1993 United Feature Syndicate, Inc.

GARFIELD SURE HAS BEEN UPSET ABOUT GETTING A YEAR OLDER

JIM DAVIS 6-17

Z

© 1994 PAWS, INC./Distributed by Universal Press Syndicate

WELL, LOOK WHO FINALLY GOT UP

JIM DAVIS 6-6

© 1994 PAWS, INC./Distributed by Universal Press Syndicate

IS IT GARFIELD, OR MISTER GRUMPY?

WE DON'T LIKE MISTER GRUMPY

AND MISTER GRUMPY DOESN'T LIKE YOU

THE BANK'S SECURITY CAMERA TOOK THIS PICTURE OF THE CULPRIT

I THOUGHT IT WAS A BAKERY!

WHERE'S MY PRESENT?

I CAN'T BRING YOU SOMETHING EVERY TIME I GO OUT

THEN WHY GO OUT?

HAVE YOU NOTICED ONE OF ODIE'S EARS IS LONGER THAN THE OTHER?

WHANG!

SPLOT!

LET'S NOT BE FORGETTING WHO'S THE CENTER OF THE UNIVERSE HERE, PAL